D0786501

How nice, dear God,
To know that You
Painted the sky
So lovely and blue!

How nice it is,
Dear God, to know
That You made trees
And flowers grow!

A Gift To Be Treasured
The Gift Of Life

Life is a miracle. A gift of God.

Have you ever wondered how a seed becomes a tender plant and grows and grows into a giant tree? How a small egg cracks open and a wet bunch of tiny feathers shakes into a new little chicken? It's a miracle, isn't it?

This is the way God created things a long time ago when He created the world and all that's in it. The oldest book ever written, the Bible, says that when God created people He "breathed into them the breath of life and man became a living soul." Since all life comes from God, life is a very sacred thing.

Your life began with the love of your mother and father. It was through them that God gave you your gift of life. Now you have a lot of choices to make about your life. And we hope you'll make all the right ones.

As you learn about life around you, the universe, the world, and the things people do in life, remember that God has given you the gift of parents and teachers to help you. Now that you are in school, you will be learning a lot of things about a lot of things. And your life will be happier and more fruitful if you learn well.

The Bible says that "loving God is the beginning of wisdom," and wisdom is the ability to make the right decisions in your life. This book has been given to you by people who believe that it is important to understand about God in order to understand fully about life. As you keep this book and read it again and again during the days and weeks ahead, you will be reminded about the important and miraculous gift you have been given – the gift of life. And you will see the many things God has done to make that life full of joy, happiness and success.

My Favorite Book

Presented By

Newberry Oil Company

Whitaker Funeral Home, Inc.

Newberry Federal

Savings & Loan Association

Thank You for the good work

you are doing with our youth.

1980

Copyrighted © 1973 by GOOD WILL PUBLISHERS Gastonia, North Carolina
Printed in the United States of America

This Is My Favorite Book

This Is Me

This Is The Way
I Write My Name

Now I lay me down to sleep,
I pray dear Lord,
my soul you'll keep
May your love be with me
through the night,
And bless me with
the morning light.

Thank you
For the world so fair,
Thank you
For the clothes we wear,
Thank you
For the food we eat,
Thank you
For the friends we meet,
Thank you
For the birds that sing,
Thank you, God,
For everything.

Dear God, help us
To do the things we should,
To be to others, kind and good;
In all we do, in all we say,
To be more loving every day.

Guide and direct me,
Show me the way;
Help me, dear Father,
All through this day.

I love the soft, soft rain,
That falls for you and me;
It helps all things to grow
And gives us drink, you see.

God made the birds
He tells them
What to do.
God loves the birds;
I know
He loves me
Too.

The cold wind
in the winter,
The pleasant summer sun,
The ripe fruits
in the garden,
God made them,
everyone.

All things, bright and beautiful,
All things, large and small,
All things, wise and wonderful,
God, our Father,
Made them all.

You put the little stars to sleep
And wake the sun each day;
I'm glad, dear God, for I'm a child
Who likes to run and play.

I'm just as glad
As I can be
That I belong
To a family.
I love my family,
Every one;
We work and play,
And we have fun.

Our home is just
The nicest place
With Mother's
Gentle, smiling face;
I'm glad for beds
That Mother makes,
And pies and puddings
That she bakes.

Daddy's strong
And loving care
Is always 'round
When I am there.
My Daddy works
And works indeed
To pay for things
That we all need.

And all of us
Help one another,
And show our love
One way or other.
I'm just as glad
As I can be
That God has given
This home to me.

Pussy willows are bursting forth
The bluebird calls, "It's spring!"
Downy chicks are peeping,
And the frogs begin to sing.
A blaze and glory of color
Each tulip and lily make;
Praise the Lord for Easter
When all the world awakes!

Thanks to God
For colors bright;
Red, orange, yellow,
Green, blue, and white.
Thanks to God
For eyes to see
The lovely things
He made for me.

The door
   At grandmother's house
   Is tall and wide.
When I ring the bell,
Grandmother comes
   And smiles and says,
   "Come inside!"

My grandfather called
From the pasture bars;
"Come, see the daisies,
They look like stars".
Sure enough, the sloping field
Twinkled in the sun
As if stars had fallen there,
I picked some, one by one.

Mother saw two
  Pretty orioles
Fly in and out
Of our big elm tree
  One day
  This spring.

Now,
They're very busy
Raising their baby birds;
Sometimes,
They're bringing food to them
In the morning
When I wake.

Sing
About my birthday!
It comes
But once a year!
Glad I am
To live and grow,
See,
And feel,
And hear!

How do friendly children play?
I know, I know.
They share their blocks
And share their toys
With other
Little girls and boys,
Because it is
The happy way.

Sometimes when morning
    Lights the sky
And gladness fills the air,
I feel like telling
    Things to God,
He seems so very near.

I'm big enough
To put my toys away,
Hang up my coat and hat;
To help my mother,
And,
To come quickly
When she calls.

Sometimes my daddy
 Works at home
To make our place
 Look trim.
And when he works
 Out in the yard,
I go along
 With him.
I pick up old bones
 My dog has left,
And bits of paper,
 While I talk;
When Daddy
 Mows the grass,
I sweep the cuttings
 Off the walk.

We went riding,
Daddy and I,
Out in the country,
Cars rushed by.

We saw a field
    Without a weed;
The farmer was at work,
    Planting seed.

God sent sunshine,
He sent rain;
We saw it again -
It was growing grain.

We saw it later,
It was golden wheat,
Soon to be bread
For someone to eat.

We had a shower
Yesterday;
And now,
The sun is shining
On our garden.
There's something
I've been wondering about.

Not long ago, I helped Daddy
Plant seeds in rows out there;
Some were such tiny little things
Some rough, some smooth.

I wonder -
How does a seed know
Just how
To become a carrot,
And not something else?
How does each seed know
Just what to be?
I *think* I know.

God has a secret
With each seed!
He talks so softly
To it in the ground,
That nothing else can hear;
He tells the seed the secret so,
That only it and He may know.

We thank you,
Dear Father,
Great and good,
We thank you
For those
Who help us have food.

God gave the sheep wool
To keep them warm.
There is wool in the cloth
Of my winter coat, new.
The wool kept the sheep warm;
It warms me now, too.

Thanksgiving Day

We plow the fields and scatter seeds,
We sow and weed the land;
But it is fed and watered
By God's almighty hand.
He sends the snow in winter,
Then spring to swell the grain,
The summer wind and sunshine
With soft, refreshing rain.
Thus comes the golden harvest,
A gift from heaven above,
And so today we thank the Lord
For all His wondrous love.

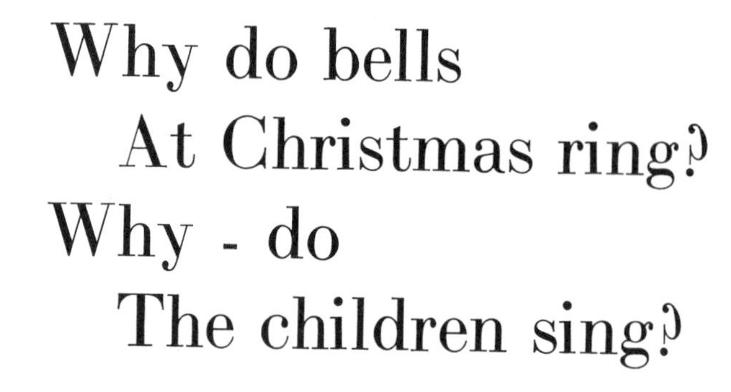

Why do bells
  At Christmas ring?
Why - do
  The children sing?

Baby Jesus lay
  In a manger bed;
Baby Jesus slept,
  Bright stars overhead.

Shepherds watched
Their sheep by night;
They watched, and saw
A wondrous sight.

Angels sang.
What did they say?
They sang,
"Jesus is born today!"
That's why
The children sing,
And joyful bells
At Christmas ring.

Wise Men found Jesus,
Led by a star;
Wise Men found Him
And brought gifts from afar.

Jesus grew
As children do;
He played and ran,
And worked hard too.